Three Kernels of Popcorn

A collection of Canadian poems

SCHOLASTIC CANADA LTD.

Canadian Cataloguing in Publication Data

Main entry under title:

Three kernels of popcorn
ISBN 1-55268-410-5

1. Children's poetry, Canadian (English).* 2. School verse, Canadian (English).*

PS8279.T5833 1999 C811'.508'09282 C98-932762-0
PR9195.27.T47 1999

5 4 3 2 1 Printed in Canada 9/9 0 1 2 3/0

Contents

Greatness

I would be the greatest poet
    the world has ever known
if only I could make you see
here on the page
sunlight
a sparrow
three kernels of popcorn
spilled on the snow

Alden Nowlan

Maples

How much of magic
still lies between
first-sipped rain
and the soon-to-follow
branch-shy showing
of the buds?

Raymond Souster

Westward through Alberta

Westward through Alberta
green and tawny
grain land, oil land
under the blue, white-dappled sky
miles of bush land
green trees silvering
when wind moves their leaves
in the summer sunlight
fields of yellow flowers,
green rounded hills,
cattle by water,
horses flicking tails.
Ten-minute stop
to walk up and down
the station platform
and stare at the grain elevator.
Then more bush
more water
grain cocks shaped
like loaves of bread
brown fields,
tractors,
a brown dirt road
going up hill.

Real woods now,
hills, valleys, chasms,
a waterfall,
purple fireweed
on the slopes.
We are out of the plains,
will wake in the mountains.
The sun has set
in the land of sunset
new world tomorrow.

Elizabeth Brewster

O earth

O earth
for the strength
in my heart
I thank thee.

O cloud
for the blood
in my body
I thank thee.

O fire
for the shine
in my eyes
I thank thee.

O sun
for the life
you gave to me
I thank thee.

Chief Dan George

Aesthetic Curiosity

Does an owl appreciate
The colour of leaves
As they fall about him
In the staggering nights of Autumn?

A.M. Klein

The Pelican

Pelican white, stroking the snowiness of his feathers,
Brightness looking at me through his beak;
Solemn, self-satisfied bird, pleased with his position
As trashman of the beach. Nature appointed, scavenger
Of his own, lonely world.

Milena Stojanac, 13

The Unicorn

Horn of ivory,
Tail of silk.
Eyes of gold,
Coat of milk.
Quick as lightning,
Old as tree.
Gentle as flower,
Raging as sea.
Dew-drop of rose,
Shadow of moon.
Mist of hills,
Cry of loon.
Memory for old,
Dream for young.
Legend for all,
Seen by none.
Horn of ivory,
Tail of silk.
Eyes of gold
And coat of milk.

Chantell Van der Ree, 13

I Wonder about Thunder

I wonder if thunder's
When angels go bowling
If the sky explodes
Because of cannon balls rolling

I wonder if thunder's
A war in the sky
When everyone's angry
But no one knows why

I wonder if thunder's
The burp of the sun
When she's had a big meal
And her supper is done

I wonder if thunder's
Just voices complaining
Because we all know
It's about to start raining

I wonder
about
THUNDER!

Sheree Fitch

The Wind

The wind is pushy
The wind is like me
I'm pushy too.
The wind makes me mad sometimes
When the wind gets under my arms
I laugh
Why does the wind come?
I'll never know.

Jenny Burton, 10

Speed Racer

Spokes like strands of
spider's web
glinted in the sun.
Strength lay hidden in graceful
metal
Cables, sinews of wire
curved to magic gears.

David Lalonde, 15

Frogs

Frogs are lumpy
and bumpy.
Frogs say Rib-it Rib-it.
If I kiss a frog will he change?
I kissed him.
His lips are slippy.

Ilyaz Yusuf, 9

Courage

Courage is when
you ask your grandfather to show you his false teeth.

And when he does
you wish you had never looked into his
empty mouth.

Katherine Clarke, 8

Bike Trail

The path
down the slope
is a zipper,
sand-coloured
in cloth of green.
I on my bike
am the tab,
gleaming in sunlight of May.
Poised at the top
I wait
and then
in a smooth descent
I glide through the soft, spring air
unzipping the coat of green.

Myra Stilborn

Sea Cliff

Wave on wave
and green on rock
and white between
the splash and black
the crash and hiss
of the feathery fall,
the snap and shock
of the water wall
and the wall of rock:
after —
after the ebb-flow,
wet rock,
high —
high over the slapping green,
water sliding away
and the rock abiding,
new rock riding
out of the spray.

A.J.M. Smith

North Country Spring

Oh! oh! the secret is out.
The poplars on the hills
Crayoned in pale green
Are declaring
That spring is here.
But, I've known for weeks.
I've picked my first blue violet
On a sunny slope,
And passed by a strawberry flower
Near the pasture gate.
And days and days ago
My friend the Saskatoon
Showed me her white spring dress.

Elizabeth Kouhi

Doggerel

There are shaggy dogs, waggy dogs
and dogs that have fleas.
There are slow dogs and low dogs
and dogs out on sprees.
There are snappy dogs,
scrappy dogs that just love a fight;
Though ruthless, if toothless,
they can't even bite.
There are swell dogs, pell-mell dogs
that race all around,
And cheap dogs and sheepdogs
and beagles and hounds.
A bassett's an asset
if you like your dogs droopy.
But it's not cool if they drool,
'cause they get you all goopy.
But the best, most caressed dog,
the one that's true blue,
Is that neat dog, that sweet dog —
the one that loves you.

Sheila Dalton

A Sailboat

A
sail
is a
white
windswept
t r i a n g l e
a
n
d
tough is the
woodenhull

Peter Garapick, 9

Like a chained dog

Like a chained dog
the wind-whipped lake
leaps again and again
for the shore.

James M. Moir

My Guilt

When I was a child I walked two miles to school
accompanied by a neighbour boy two years
younger.
Freddie was fat and freckle faced
with wheat-straw hair and a mean stepmother.
It was late fall and one day his father
bought him a new winter cap.
It was made of heavy brown tweed with ear flaps.
It cost one dollar and twenty cents.
The next morning when he joined me
on the way to school, he showed me his new cap.
Almost bursting with pride, he took it off
so I could see the rabbit fur lining the ear flaps.
Whether out of downright meanness, or jealousy
because I didn't have a new cap,
just last year's old red knitted toque,
I snatched it out of his hand
tossing it in the air and catching it again.
This went on for about half a mile.
Screaming and pleading, he ran after me.
But his legs were shorter than mine
he couldn't catch me.
Winded, I stopped and thrust the cap down
a badger hole.

He ran up sobbing and reached down
into the earth.
But the hole was deep, his arm not long enough.
He sat back on his heels and cried bitterly.
Guiltily, I stretched my arm down,
but there was no bottom, or so it appeared.
"Come on," I said. "We'll be late for school,
we'll get it on our way home tonight."
All day I felt his troubled gaze upon me
and I had trouble focusing on the printed page.
When we trudged homeward after school,
we tried again to rescue the cap, with no success.
And since Freddie was not allowed to loiter,
nor was I, we gave up.
Freddie dragged his feet, dreading to face
his stepmother and I too cowardly
to confess my guilt.
Later that evening his father took a shovel
and dug, but the hole was deep, slanting off
in different directions underground.
He gave up too and Freddie cried himself to sleep.
After that he came to school bareheaded.
My heart was like a stone in my breast
when I looked at his ears red with cold.
But I had no money to buy him another cap
even had I wanted to, which I suppose I didn't.

They moved away after that, not because of the cap,
but drought, poverty and all that goes with it
drove them to another part of the country.
Through the many years since,
Freddie's sad face haunts me accusingly
and rightly so, for the callous thing I had done,
when I was twelve and he was ten.

Agnes Copithorne

Redwoods

Redwoods,
ancient, giantific structures
steadily creeping upward
toward the silent regions,
standing dignified
in the mist
with expansive branches
like a reddish dinosaur
that turned into a tree.

Batul Somani, 10

A Summer Night

Night falls in the garden.
A soft breeze rustles
The leaves on the trees.
The frog croaks in the bullrushes
By the pond,
And crickets chirp noisily nearby.
The grass is soaked with
A sprinkling of dew.
The moon comes out and
Shines with an unearthly glow.
Suddenly a bird
Bursts into song,
Then all is still again.
And then, when the first glimmer of light
Appears on the horizon,
You can see
Night coming out of the garden.

Sally Ormerod, 11

Kittens

Kittens are
frizzy
fuzzy
fluffy
All in a ball,
squirmy
squeezy
And very small.
I love kittens
and that is all!

Kathy Hrinivich, 8

Four Hungry Babies

Four hungry babies
squawking.
Two worms.
Do robins learn arithmetic?

Grade 2 class

Secrets

Some things are for telling
Some things are for yelling
Some things are for whispering
To flowers or the sky
Other secrets wing their way
To light by and by

Sheree Fitch

The Six-Quart Basket

The six-quart basket
one side gone
half the handle torn off
sits in the centre of the lawn
and slowly fills up
with the white fruits of the snow.

Raymond Souster

A Peaceful Picture

Two cuddly Kittens
Comfily, cosily curled
Close together
Sleeping so silently
On a bed of cosy clothes
Close together
Quiet, queenly, crying not
Sweet and silent, purring peacefully
Close together
Clean, cute, comforting
Quiet chorales of peaceful purring
Close together
Sleepy sonatas of silent wonder
Wordless wisdom, blue-eyed beauty
Close together

Sharyn Manuel, 10

My black crow

My black crow hunts
for bird-seed in the bird-tray
in my neighbour's yard

Madonna Mayfield, 9

Blossoms

Clusters of blossoms
    Opening very softly
        On the grey branches

Victoria Rawle, 9

Trees

The trees are bending
Whispering to each other,
Passing out secrets.

Janet Vanderpost, 9

Summer Passes

The wayside aster splashes its bright blue
Along the dusty road; the Queen Anne lace
Foams colt-high in the pastures, frosty white;
Late summer strolls with slow and leisured pace
And in quiet wood where it's cool and damp,
Delphinium lifts up its pale blue lamp.
The shorn wheat fields now lie, like gold-bronze rugs,
In rustling taffeta; green glows the corn;
The meadowlark with silver-fluted throat
Sings sweetly still, though misty now the morn.
But when the grackle gleans, then clouds the sky;
Brown thrasher, thrush and lark soon say good-bye.

Prairie Gardener

The Tale of Canadian Jim

You might know the name of Canadian Jim.
He's a dog of some fame and renown.
But there was a time I remember quite well
When he came to reside in our town.

Canadian Jim had a head full of dreams
He always had a plan in his pocket
And so, when one morning he passed
  a high fence,
He made up his mind he would walk it.

He climbed on the fence and at first
  he fell off.
At the start he was tippy and slow.
But he practiced and soon an idea
  took shape;
He decided to put on a show!

He learned how to walk down the fence,
  did our Jim.
He was limber, and nimble, and spry.
He perfected a twirl and a leap for the end
And he invited the crowds to drop by.

When the crowd was in place, he performed
on the fence
All dressed up in his very best collar.
So fine was the show that the group
soon agreed
When he asked if they might pay a dollar.

The crowd came each day with great pleasure
to watch
Our friend Jim, who had mastered the fence.
Because they were regulars, Jim said all right
When they asked to pay just fifty cents.

Now, Jim grew more expert. He added a jig.
And the show became longer (not shorter).
But Jim so enjoyed it, the crowd
rightly guessed
He would still do his show for a quarter.

A picture of grace he became before long.
A master of movement and mime.
He made it seem easy
(Of course, it was not.)
And they soon offered Jim just a dime.

They promised to pay him a dime
    from then on,
But townsfolk are terribly fickle.
And if you know townsfolk,
    (and if you know rhymes),
You'll know they soon paid him a nickel.

By now he was famous, Canadian Jim!
His audience numbered so many.
"Reward in itself!" as the crowd did explain
When they said they would pay him a penny.

Jim heard their new offer from up
        on that fence
And answered with something quite clever.
"I will take your penny,
        and here's what you'll see.
For a penny I'll leave here forever!"

Barbara Nichol

My brother and I

If we were good friends,
we would talk to each other,
but since we're related,
you're only my brother.
We share the same roof,
the same clothes, the same bike,
and to think we rode
on the very same trike.
We see each other every day,
and love each other in a small private way.
If we were good friends,
we would talk to each other,
but since we're related,
you're only my brother.

Joan Turchan, 10

Turn the lamp on

Turn the lamp on, Mother, dear,
The night is fearful black.
Put the light on, Mother, dear,
So Daddy will come back.
I'll turn the lantern on, my son,
The house will be a-light.
But, oh my darling, Daddy will
Not journey back tonight.
He ran into a skunk today
So darling, run to bed.
I will not let him in with us
He'll use the barn, instead!

Fran Newman

Fade Out

The vanishing cream I've been using for weeks
To fade all those ugly brown spots
That cover my chin and my forehead and cheeks
Has turned out to be not so hot.

The cream sure is vanishing, that much I'll say
But boy, has it made me look weird!
Instead of it taking my freckles away,
The rest of my face disappeared!

Mary Blakeslee

My Quilt

My quilt is made of animal skins.
The lions roar at me,
I can hear the tiger and leopards fighting,
And the skunk smells.

Marjorie Irwin, 9

Terriers

Poodles go prancing on pedicured paws.
Setters are fleet as a song.
Wolfhounds stalk haughtily. Corgis cavort.
But terriers trundle along.
Cockers have amber eyes limpid with love.
Collies look tragic and wise.
A Labrador's gaze is benignly adult
But you can't find a terrier's eyes.
Some dogs are mammoth and some are minute.
A Peke you can pocket with ease
While a Saint Bernard stands as high as your waist.
Terriers just come to your knees.
All dogs are watchdogs. A dog worth his salt
His home and his hearthfire defends.
He'll bark at a burglar, or breadman or boy!
But terriers growl at their friends.
Some dogs have beauty and some dogs have brains.
Tricks some are capable of.
There are show dogs and sheepdogs and gun dogs
    and guides.
But terriers know about love.

Jean Little

Amnesia

I said my speech today.

It started
"Honorable judges
and fellow classmates."

It ended
"Thank you for listening."

Funny thing is
I can't remember what was in between
except that
Jimmy snickered
Sarah grinned
Jeremy shot some eraser
and it had something to do with gerbils.

Diane Dawber

First Snow

Let the first
snow fall
white upon
fields and the
roofs of the
houses
freshly.
Let it remain a
time on them,
covering
all of the
dust, and the
dried-up
leaves of the
fire-weeds,
hiding old
traces;
making all
new, for a time.

W. W. E. Ross

After the Hurricane

After the hurricane
nothing private can be found.
The washcloth is full
of nails. Toothpaste
is spattered
all over the fire hydrants.
A power mower hangs
from the ceiling
of an elm, turning its blades
as nothing else desires to do.
Women gather under it,
marvelling. Boy Scouts
climb for it. Ditch-diggers
wager when it will run out of gas.
It has elected itself President.
Something or nothing
is happening
everywhere. Clothes on the line
have become avocadoes;
telephone poles, paperclips.

Everywhere the curbs
are breaking up. People
hunt dogs in the street.
Their homes have run away
into the sky.
Their umbrellas are hungry.

Jack W. Thomas

Sadness Is a Road

Sadness is a long, black, dirty pavement
With white lines sometimes on it.
It is hard,
Rough stuff;
Smells of tar;
Sounds like Sh-Sh-Sh
As cars pass by fast . . .
Sadness is a long, black, lonely thing.

Michelle Kenrick, 10

Spring

Spring is like an elastic breaking
After winter stretches it.

Greg Nielsen, 9

November

Snow
and
night
come
down
into
the
last
yellow
ledge
of
sky
geese
fly
higher
than
the
sun

Anne Corkett

In a Sacred Way

Being Indian has nothing to do with
having a status card
the colour of your eyes
if you live on a reserve
if you wear moccasins
or work for the Assembly of First Nations
being Indian is how you live each day.

Rose

Alone

Imagine an island
Deserted and lonely
Out on the ocean, alone.
Imagine a ship
All full of people
Sailing the ocean, alone.
Imagine a storm
Wild and raging
Over the ocean, alone.
Imagine a person
Floating on wreckage
To the island, alone.
Imagine a week
A month, a year
Living off tropical fruit, alone.
Imagine a rescue
After many years
Of living, alone.

Jen Khashmanian, 13

Prairie Harvest

Choking dust and chaff
Hang in dense clouds
Over the threshing machine.
Weary, grimy men
Struggle in vain,
To satisfy
The gulping monster's hunger.
Long into the day
It chews and grinds
The bundles
As fast as they are stuffed
Into the gaping mouth.
The food is swallowed
With noisy, impolite gulps,
Followed by
Metallic belches.
The mouth opens again
To show gnashing teeth
It is hopeless to try to fill,
This grotesque cavity.
Weary, hungry men,
Their muscles aching,
Turn from the enemy
Toward home.

Claire Wolf, 12

my friend

my friend is
like bark
rounding a tree
he warms
like sun
on a winter day
he cools
like water
in the hot noon
his voice
is ready
as a spring bird
he is
my friend
and I
am his

Emily Hearn

Rain

Rain is as mischief-making as a child.
She pokes the Thunder's ribs until he roars.
She sits on steepled roofs and thrums her heels
And tickles grass and taps at solemn doors.
She dampens dignitaries and their wives,
Paints saucy freckle-faces on the roads,
Makes mud puddles and rainbows; then gets down
To scrub the tiny blissful backs of toads.

Jean Little

What Is in a Name?

Killer is a friendly dog.
Rusty isn't red.
If Sporty had his way he'd spend
From dawn to dusk in bed.

Rover never leaves the yard.
Waggins has no tail.
Tiny is so big she eats
Her dinner from a pail.

Fluffy's coat is very thin
Racer's rather slow.
Lucky's had a bee sting now
Two summers in a row.

Happy tends to howl a lot.
Marauder's very tame.
And Mister is a lady dog.
So what is in a name?

Barbara Nichol

I Pulled an "A"

I pulled an "A" in math today
It took a bit of work,
I highly recommend it, though —
Your parents go berserk.

It's not enough to buy you stuff
To celebrate your grade,
They also grant you privileges
For this great mark you've made.

Your mom cooks all your favourite foods.
Your dad makes "genius" jokes.
An "A" in math sure makes it tough
To recognize your folks.

Your sister does the dishes, and
Your brother rakes the yard.
I'll get an "A" again one day —
That's if it's not too hard.

Gordon Korman

Rapunzel

Rapunzel, Rapunzel, let down your fair hair,
I'll hoist myself up on your braid.
Rapunzel, Rapunzel, move swiftly, my dear.
Oh, hurry, my lovely young maid!

So lovely Rapunzel let down her fine hair
(For she surely adored this brave lad!),
But alas for the lovers, he weighed such a lot . . .
What a nice double funeral they had!

Fran Newman

The Man from Milwaukee

There once was a man from Milwaukee,
Who loved nothing better than hockey.
Because he was small
And could skate not at all,
He ended up life as a jockey.

Richard S. Graham, 9

A Young Man from Old Montreal

A young man from old Montreal
Went out to a fancy dress ball.
He thought he could risk it
Dressed up as a biscuit
But a dog ate him up in the hall.

Anonymous

The Bratty Brother (Sister)

I dumped the bratty brother
In the shark-infested sea;
By dusk the sea was empty, and
The brat was home with me.

I mailed the bratty brother
To a jail in Moosonee,
The sobbing jailer mailed him back
The next day, COD.

I wept, and hurled the bratty
Brother off the CN Tower;
He lolloped through the living room
In less than half an hour.

So now I keep my brother
In the furnace, nice and neat.
I can't wait till December
When my Dad turns on the heat.

Dennis Lee

Computer Rap

When I saw my computer
For the very first time,
I couldn't make sense of it
Or reason or rhyme.

I had no clue
About menu or file.
Thought the computer
Just wasn't my style.

Then I hit a few keys
And on came the lights.
The screen flashed on
To some wonderful sights.

The latest high fashions,
Some very cool art,
A new book on hockey,
That was only a start.

Undersea travel,
Jokes in your face,
What a great thing
For the whole human race.

I'm in tune with the world
And haven't you heard,
You don't have to be
A computer nerd.

It's fantastic, it's fun
No sweat and no strife.
This fabulous thing's
Taken over my life.

Sonja Dunn

The Secret Place

There's a place I go, inside myself,
        Where nobody else can be,
And none of my friends can tell it's there —
        Nobody knows but me.

It's hard to explain the way it feels,
        Or even where I go.
It isn't a place in time or space,
        But once I'm there, I know.

It's tiny, it's shiny, it can't be seen,
        But it's as big as the sky at night . . .
I try to explain and it hurts my brain
        But once I'm there, it's right.

There's a place I know inside myself,
        And it's neither big or small,
And whenever I go, it feels as though
        I never left at all.

Dennis Lee

The Sun

Like a mighty king
Shining in a radiant suit of gold armour,
The sun rises
Over the top of the horizon.

Slowly he climbs higher
And higher and higher,
His gold armour
Growing even more radiant
Until he reaches
The very top.

Then the mighty king
In all his glory
Rules the land
Till the evening
When he sinks from his throne
And becomes duller and duller
Finally vanishing from sight.

Beryl Penner, 11

The Lighthouse

It stands proud and tall,
sending its
shimmering light across
the water.
From inside you can hear the
pounding surf against the rocks,
its strong walls making you feel
warm and secure.

The smell of the wet cobblestones
seeps through the cracks.
The touch of the water makes
you shiver with cold.

Michael McMillen, 11

The Mountains of Saskatchewan

Try to imagine mountains
where waves of wheat
resemble oceans
and black soil is richer
than jagged mountain jade.

Try to imagine mountains
with storm clouds
low on the horizon
the sun glowing behind
those dark shapes.

Try to imagine mountains
where every rise of land
is called a hill
and every hill dreams it is a mountain.

Try
to imagine mountains
where there are no mountains
to lean against
for shade.

Mick Burrs

The Earth and the People

The earth was here before the people.
The very first people
came out of the ground.
Everything came from the ground,
even caribou.
Children once grew
out of the ground
just as flowers do.
Women out wandering
found them sprawling on the grass
and took them home and nursed them.
That way people multiplied.
This land of ours
has become habitable
because we came here
and learned how to hunt.

Traditional Inuit Song

round slice of moon

round slice of moon: December night
stark branches lift
from hollowed black to silvered white
    no wind disturbs

the stars swing by in frozen flight
soft smoke floats thin
from fires alight in rooms below
    the stillness holds

in silent snow
neat footprints write a winter's tale
    the night dreams on

Fran Newman

Acknowledgements

For reprint permission grateful acknowledgement is made to:

Academic Press Canada for "First Snow" from SHAPES AND SOUNDS by W.W.E. Ross. Reprinted by permission of Academic Press Canada.

All About Us for "Four Hungry Babies" from ALL ABOUT US; "Spring" by Greg Neilsen and "The Wind" by Jennifer Burton, from MY THIRD EYE.

Anne Burns for "Summer Passes" from GLISTENING IN THE SUN.

Mick Burrs for "The Mountains of Saskatchewan" from JUMBO GUMBO: SONGS, POEMS AND STORIES FOR CHILDREN.

Canadian Author & Bookman for "Like a chained dog" by James Moir (Winter 1975).

The Canadian Council of Teachers of English Language Arts for "Frogs" by Ilyaz Yusuf, "Kittens" by Kathy Hrinivich, "My Quilt" by Marjorie Irwin, "Prairie Harvest" by Claire Wolf, "Sadness Is a Road" by Michelle Kenrick, "A sailboat" by Peter Garapick, from ZODIAC; "Courage" by Katherine Clarke, "My brother and I" by Joan Turchan, from PANDORA'S BOX; "Blossoms" by Victoria Rawle, "The Lighthouse" by Michael McMillen, "The Man from Milwaukee" by Richard S. Graham, "My black crow" by Madonna Mayfield, "Redwoods" by Batul Somani, "Speed Racer" by David Lalonde, "A Summer Night" by Sally Ormerod, "The Sun" by Beryl Penner, "Trees" by Janet Vanderpost, "The Unicorn" by Chantell Van der Ree, from MYSTERIOUS SPECIAL SAUCE. Reprinted by permission of the Canadian Council of Teachers of English Language Arts.

Agnes Copithorne for "My Guilt."

Anne Corkett for "November" from SALAMANDER'S LAUGHTER AND OTHER POEMS.

Sheila Dalton for "Doggerel."

Doubleday Canada Limited for "I Wonder About Thunder" and "Secrets" by Sheree Fitch from TOES IN MY NOSE AND OTHER POEMS. Reproduced by permission of Doubleday Canada.

Sonja Dunn for "Computer Rap."

Hancock House for "O earth" by Chief Dan George from MY HEART SOARS by Chief Dan George and Helmet Hirnshall, published by Hancock House Publishers, Ltd.

HarperCollins for "The Secret Place" from THE ICE CREAM STORE by Dennis Lee. Published by HarperCollins Publishers Ltd. © 1991 by Dennis Lee.

Irwin Publishing for "Greatness" from THE MYSTERIOUS NAKED MAN © 1969 Alden Nowlan. Used by permission.

ITP Nelson for "my friend" by Emily Hearn from HOCKEY CARDS & HOPSCOTCH © 1971. Reprinted by permission of Nelson Canada, a division of International Thomson.

Jen Khashmanian for "Alone."

Gordon Korman for "I Pulled an 'A.'"

Elizabeth Kouhi for "North Country Spring," first published by Penumbra Press.

Jean Little for "Rain" and "Terriers" from WHEN THE PIE WAS OPENED.

Sharyn Manuel for "A Peaceful Picture."

McClelland and Stewart Inc. for "Sea Cliff" by A.J.M. Smith from THE SACRED SHADE. Reprinted by permission of McClelland and Stewart Inc., The Canadian Publishers.

Na-Me-Res (Native Men's Residence) for "In a Sacred Way" by Rose, from STEAL MY RAGE, edited by Joel T. Maki.

Fran Newman for "Rapunzel" and "Turn the lamp on."

Oberon Press for "Maples" and "The Six-Quart Basket" by Raymond Souster from THE COLLECTED POEMS OF RAYMOND SOUSTER; and "Westward Through Alberta" from SELECTED POEMS OF ELIZABETH BREWSTER. Reprinted by permission of Oberon Press.

OWL, the Canadian magazine for children, for "The Pelican" © Milena Stojanac, Fredericton, N.B.

Quarry Press for "Amnesia" by Diane Dawber from MY UNDERWEAR'S INSIDE OUT!

Scholastic-TAB Publications for "Fade Out" by Mary Blakeslee from IT'S TOUGH TO BE A KID and "round slice of moon" by Fran Newman from SUNFLAKES & SNOWSHINE.

Myra Stilborn for "Bike Trail."

Stoddart Publishing for "The Tale of Canadian Jim" and "What Is in a Name" by Barbara Nichol from BISCUITS IN THE CUPBOARD. Reprinted by permission of Stoddart Publishing Co. Limited, Don Mills, Ont.

University of Toronto Press Incorporated for "Aesthetic Curiosity" from THE COLLECTED POEMS OF A.M. KLEIN © 1974 McGraw-Hill Ryerson Limited. Reprinted by permission.

Waves for "After the Hurricane" by Jack W. Thomas, originally published in *Waves*.

Westwood Creative Artists for "The Bratty Brother (Sister)" from GARBAGE DELIGHT by Dennis Lee (Macmillan of Canada, 1997). Copyright © 1977 Dennis Lee. With permission of the author.

The publisher has attempted to contact all rights holders for permission to reprint. In some cases current rights holders could not be located. If updated information is received, it will be included in the next printing.